TIME FLIES

ERIC ROHMANN

SCHOLASTIC INC.
New York   Toronto   London   Auckland   Sydney

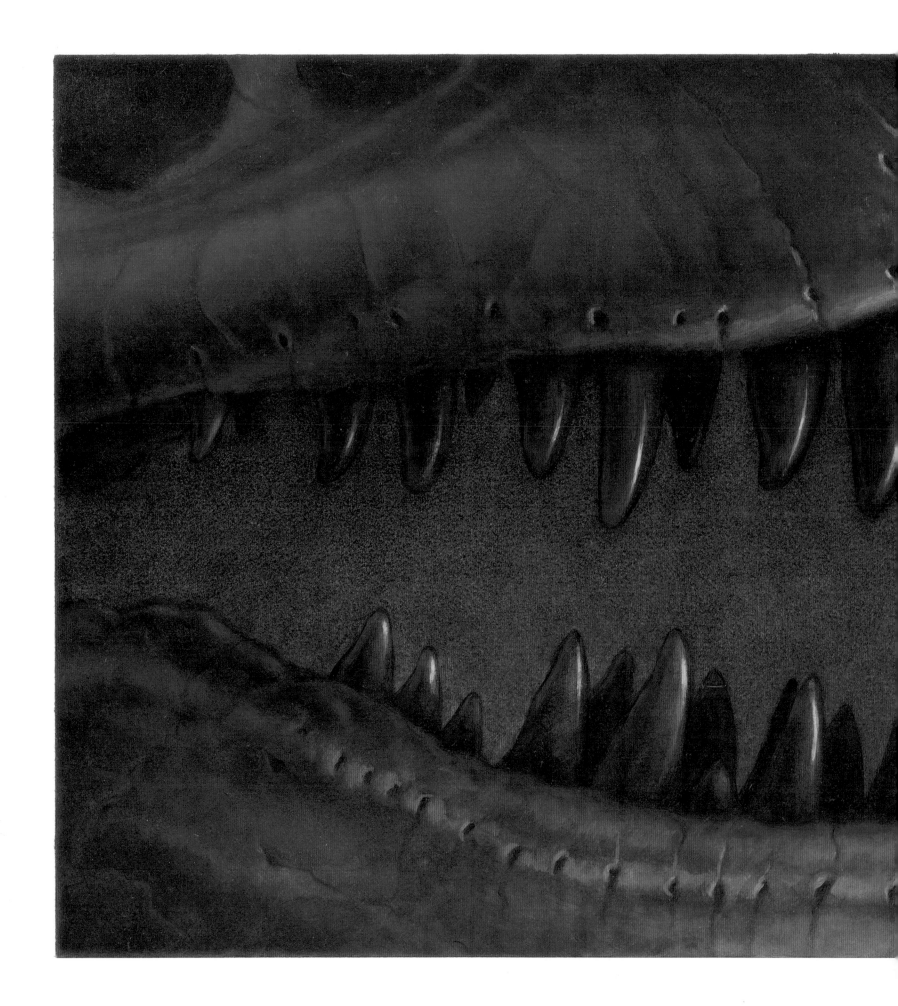

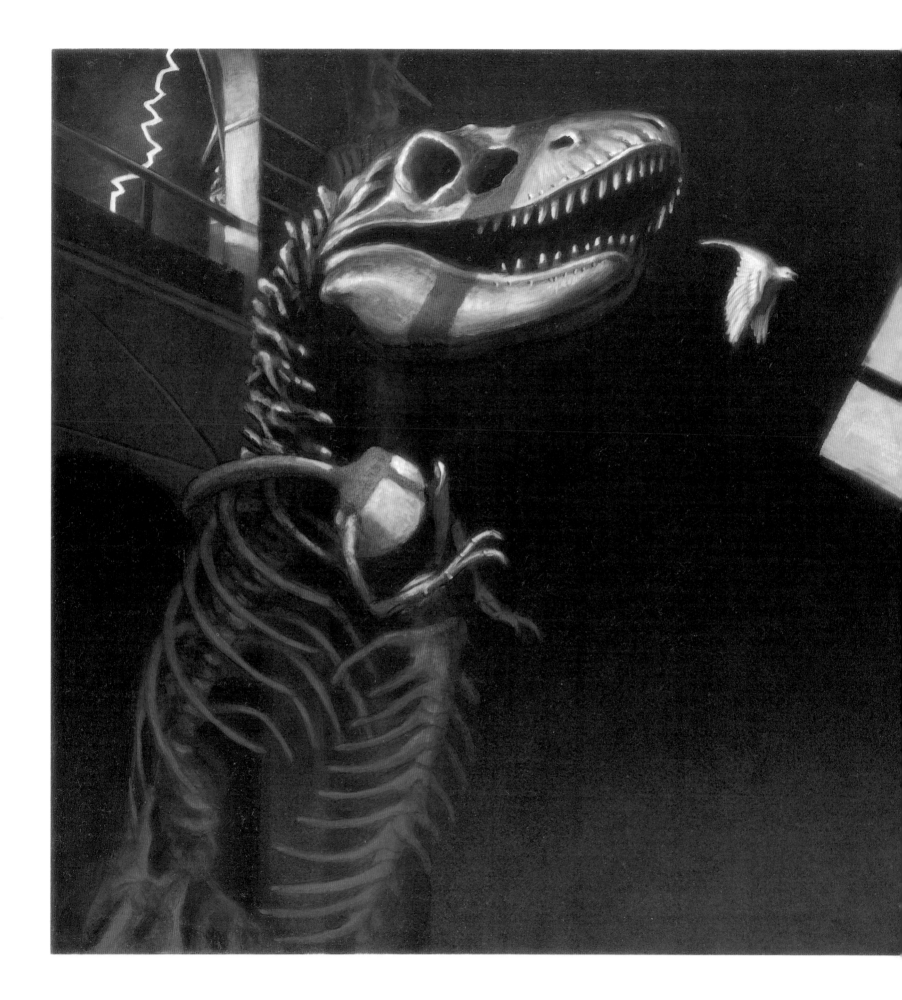

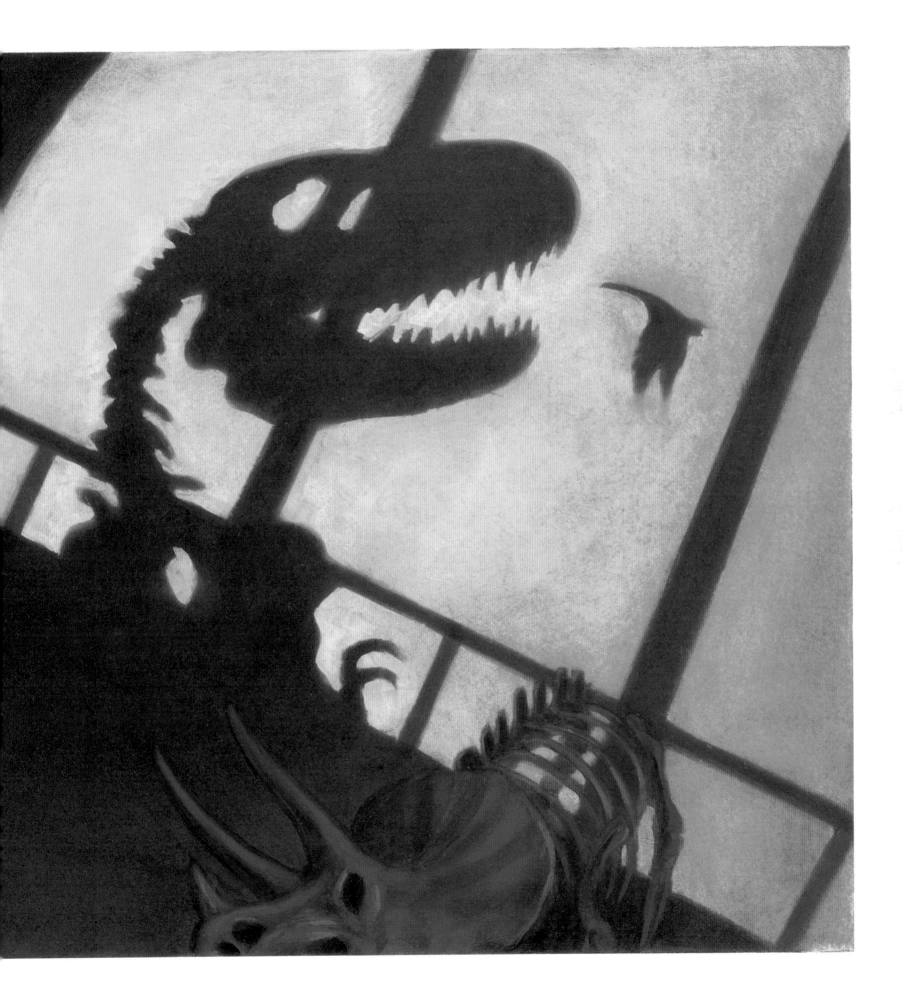

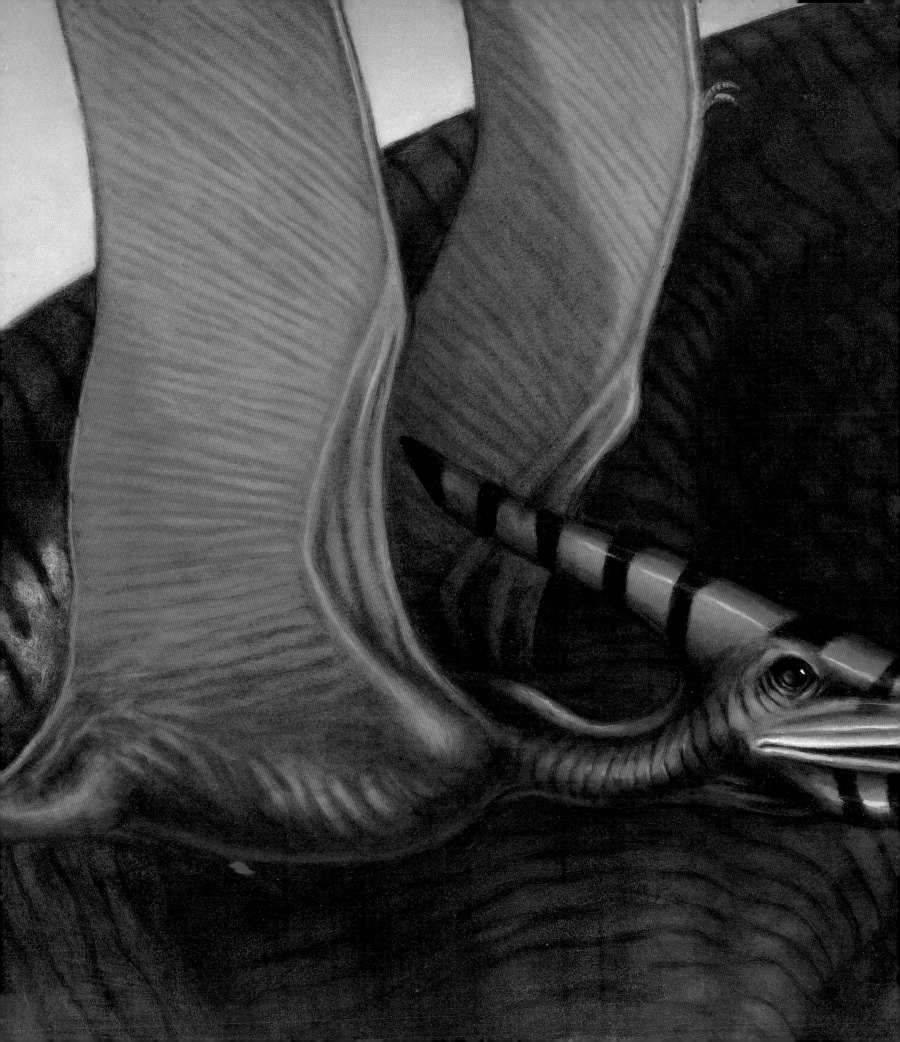

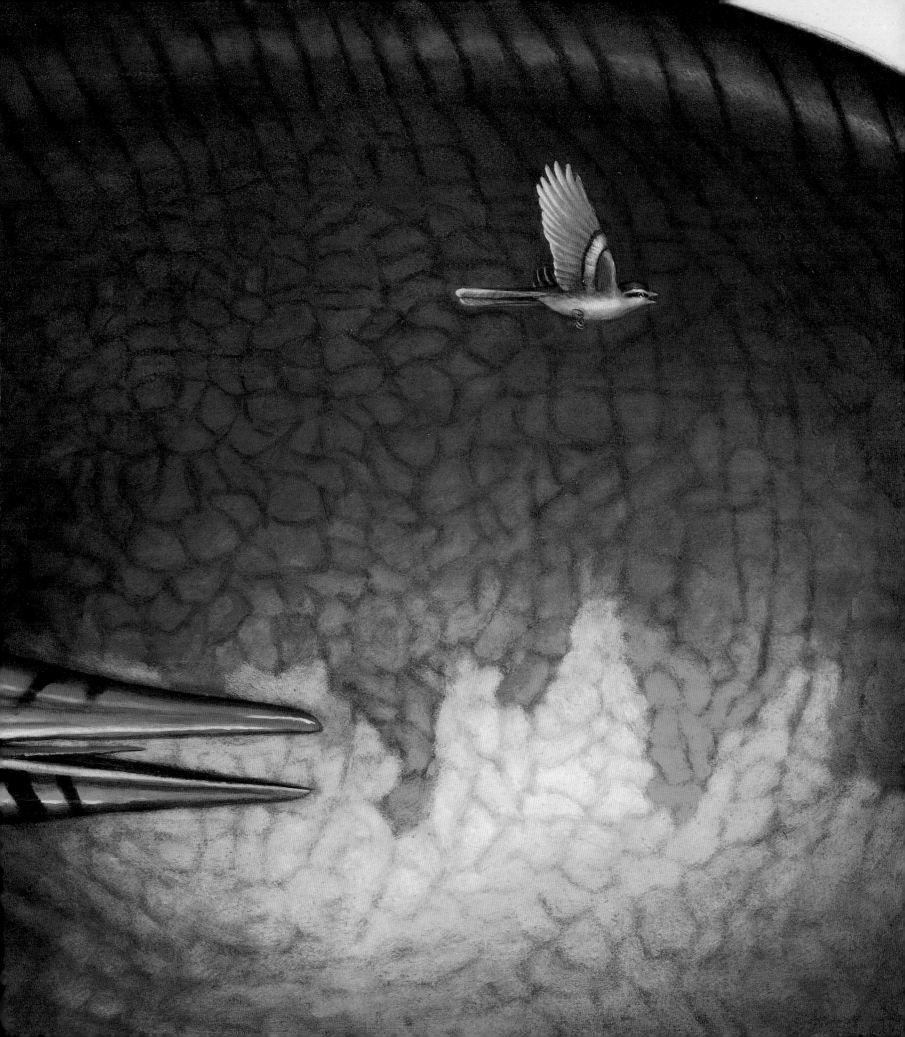

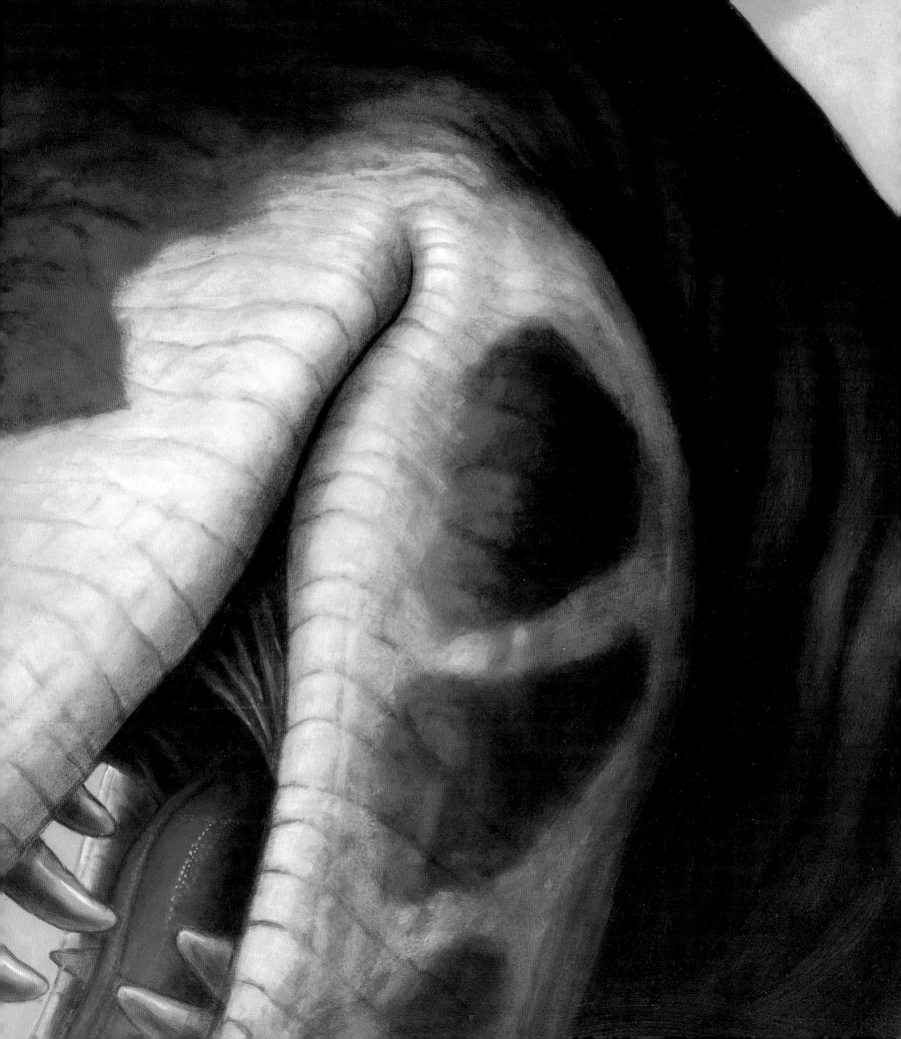

ISBN 0-590-59784-1

Copyright © 1994 by Eric Rohmann.
All rights reserved. Published by Scholastic Inc., 555 Broadway, New York, NY 10012, by arrangement with Crown Publishers, Inc., a Random House company.

12 11 10 9 8 7 6 5 4 3 2 1   5 6 7 8 9/9 0/0

Printed in the U.S.A.   08
First Scholastic printing, September 1995